SECRET CODEBOOK

THE BEANObooks
geddes & grosset

BE A CHAMPION CODE CRACKER
LIKE ME! THIS BOOK TELLS YOU ALL
YOU NEED TO KNOW!

PART ONE

SIMPLE LETTER CODES

Writing a message in code is a simple way of keeping it secret. Only the sender and the person who knows how to decipher the message will be able to understand it. The name given to making coded messages is cryptography—which means 'secret writing'.

There are thousands of different kinds of secret writing, so there are really two important things about writing in code:

1 Putting the message into code.
2 Making sure that the person who receives the message knows what the code is—otherwise he or she might never be able to work out the message.

3

Project

Your first simple code

The simplest type of code is one that changes or shifts all the letters in the original message. Suppose the message you want to write is:

WILL MEET YOU AFTER CLASS

Write this down on a spare piece of paper. Now write down the coded message using the next letter in the alphabet for each letter in the original message. Thus 'W' would become 'X', 'I' would become 'J', and so on. The coded message becomes:

XJMM NFFU ZPV BGUFS DMBTT

Unless you have agreed that you will always use this code, you still want to add something that tells the person who gets the message what the code is. The simplest way to do this is to show what 'A' has become in the code. 'A' has become 'B', and all the other letters have been shifted on one, so the key letter to this code is 'B'. We can add this to the message either at the beginning:

BXJMM NFFU ZPV BGUFS DMBTT

or at the end:

XJMM NFFU ZPV BGUFS DMBTTB

BREAKING THE CODE

This simple code is, however, quite easy to 'break' or decode without knowing the key. If you got hold of a message like this, which was not intended for you, you would know at once that it was in code. The simplest type of code is just a shift of letters in the alphabet, as we have learnt. This would be the first thing to try to 'break' the code. The first, or last, letter in the message might well be the 'key', so we would try this first and see if the message makes sense.

5

MAKING THE CODE MORE DIFFICULT

To stop the code being broken too easily, we must make it a little more difficult. We can agree with the person to whom we are sending the message to hide the key letter in a different place, say at the end of the first word, or at the beginning of the second word, in every message. We can also use a shift of more than one letter along the alphabet, which will make the code more difficult to guess. Suppose we use a shift of three letters along the alphabet. 'A' becomes 'D', 'B' becomes 'E', and so on. When we run out of alphabet letters, we start again with A. Thus 'W' becomes 'Z', 'X' becomes 'A', 'Y' becomes 'B' and 'Z' becomes 'C'. The key letter is 'D' ('A' becomes 'D' in the code).

Now let us see what the message looks like:

ZLOOD PHHW BRX DIWHU FODVV

You will see that we have hidden the key letter at the end of the first word.

Project

Backwards or forwards

Work out your own code messages using a forward shift of a certain number of letters. Also make a code by a shift backwards. You could make 'A' become 'Z', 'B' become 'A', and so on, which is a shift of one letter backwards. The key letter in this case would be 'Z'.

Remember that the bigger the shift, that is, the greater the number of letters you move along, the more difficult it will be for anyone else to break the code, unless they know where to look for the key letter. You could use the same code all the time, then you need not include the key letter. This will give anyone else more practice at breaking the code, however, so it is best to change the code after using it for a few messages.

The bigger the shift the more likely you are to make mistakes in writing out the message in

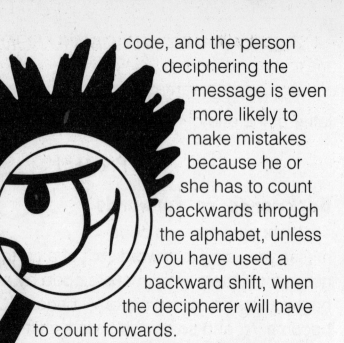

code, and the person deciphering the message is even more likely to make mistakes because he or she has to count backwards through the alphabet, unless you have used a backward shift, when the decipherer will have to count forwards.

It helps, both when writing a coded message and decoding it, to write out the letters of the alphabet in a line. You can then count any shift accurately with the point of a pencil (figure 1).

A MORE DIFFICULT VARIATION

Anybody who really takes trouble can always break a simple letter shift code,

(figure 1)

A B C D E F G H I J K L M N O P Q R S T U V W X Y Z

although it will take time and patience. We can make it much more difficult for the 'enemy' to decode our secret messages if we use a different shift for each word. He or she may break the code and decipher the first word, but when this is tried on the second word it does not make sense because the code is different for this word.

The addition of key letters could give the game away, so we can adopt a general rule:

The first word will have a one-letter shift
The second word will have a two-letter shift
The third word will have a three-letter shift, etc.

Starting with the original message:

WILL MEET YOU AFTER CLASS
this now becomes:

XJMM OGGV BRX
(one-letter shift) (two-letter shift) (three-letter shift)

  EJXIV   HQFXX
  (four-letter shift) (five-letter shift)

Different shifts

Work out other ways of using different shifts for each word.

You could start the other way round by using one shift for the last word, two shifts for the next to last word, and so on. How about the actual date as the key to the shifts—2 March 1996 would become 2–3–1–9–9–6. If there are more words than this in the message, simply repeat the same shifts.

LETTER GROUPS

Splitting up the coded message into letter groups also makes it more difficult to break, because it no longer looks like words. It makes even a simple shift code look much more complicated.

For example, we worked out the following as a single shift coded message with the key letter included:

Message: WILL MEET YOU AFTER CLASS
Code: BXJMM NFFU ZPV BGUFS DMBTT

Split this up into groups of five letters and it

looks even more difficult to break. You will find that making a coded message look complicated will put many people off trying to break it.

BXJMM NFFUZ PVBGU FSDMB TT

Note that we have ended up with only two letters in the last group. It might have been one, or three, or four. We can fill in the gaps with letters that do not mean anything, to make up a complete group. Better still, add a false key letter as the end letter in this group. This could put anyone off who knew a bit about codes and was looking for a key letter here.

Project

Your diary in code

You can use codes to record
as well as send secret messages. Why not
keep your diary in code, or at least the more
secret parts of it can be written in code. Then if
it gets into the wrong hands, your secrets
should still be safe!

PART TWO

KEYWORD CODES

These are really the same as simple letter shift codes except that they are based on a key word instead of a shift of letters along the alphabet. They take a bit more working out, and decoding when you get such a message, but they are a lot more difficult to break if you do not know the key word.

The best way to explain a key word code is to work through an example step by step. Suppose the message is ARE YOU GOING OUT TONIGHT WITH ME, and the key word you are using is CODEPROJECT.

A key word can be one word, or two or more words run together. Write down the key word first.

CODEPROJECT

Under this write down numbers, starting with '1' under the first letter of the alphabet that appears in the key word, 2 for the second letter, and so on. There is no A or B in our key word, so C is the first letter. Put 1 under the first C. Now C appears again later in the key word, so this is marked 2.

CODEPROJECT
1   2

'D' is the next letter, so this takes number 3. The first 'E' comes next and takes 4, so the second 'E' will be 5, thus:

CODEPROJECT
1   3 4   5 2

'J' is next in the alphabet, taking 6, and so on, to end up like this:

C O D E P R O J E C T
1   7   3   4   9 10   8   6   5   2 11

Project

A table using your code

Now draw up a table, as shown in figure 2. Write down the key word, and under this the numbers you have just worked out. Draw vertical lines to separate the key word letters and numbers into columns. Then draw horizontal lines, starting with a line under the numbers and then three more lines to make squares under the numbers.

(figure 2)

C	O	D	E	P	R	O	J	E	C	T
1	7	3	4	9	10	8	6	5	2	11
2	8	4								
3	9	5								
4	10	6								

Write the message in these squares, as shown in figure 3.

The coded message is then written out by reading down the columns, starting with the column marked 1, then 2, and so on.

Column 1 is written down AOI.

Column 2, almost at the other end of the table, is NT.

(figure 3)

C	O	D	E	P	R	O	J	E	C	T
1	7	3	4	9	10	8	6	5	2	11
A	R	E	Y	O	U	G	O	I	N	G
O	U	T	T	O	N	I	G	H	T	W
I	T	H	M	E						

The complete message written out in this way is:

AOI NT ETH YTM IH OG RUT GI OOE UN GW

That is going to be very difficult to decode for anyone who does not know the key word. We started with a message of seven words, but in the coded message there are eleven 'words', so there is no chance of guessing single words. Also all the 'words' are three or two letters, which makes it even more complicated.

KNOWING THE KEY WORD

Is this message easy to decode when you know the key word? Yes, it is. The person receiving the message writes down the key word, then works out the numbers to go under each letter, just as in figure 2, drawing vertical and horizontal lines to complete the 'boxes'.

The decoder has a clue as to how many horizontal lines to draw from the number of letters in the coded 'words'. No code 'word' has more than three letters, so he or she will not need more than three lines. It does not matter if more are drawn. They will simply remain blank.

Having drawn out the 'boxes', the decoder then starts to write down the code words in columns, beginning in column 1, then column

(figure 4)

C	O	D	E	P	R	O	J	E	C	T
1	7	3	4	9	10	8	6	5	2	11
A		E							N	
O		T							T	
I		H								

2, and so on (figure 4). In the end the decoder has got to the same drawing as the sender made (figure 3) and can therefore then read back the message.

Project

Changing the key word

You can work out any number of different codes in the way described. For the same starting message, each different key word will give a different code message.

Use short key words and a larger number of horizontal lines and 'boxes' to give code 'words' with a greater number of letters in each. This makes it simpler to code and decode the message, for you do not have to work out the numbers for so many columns.

Use the word PROJECT as the key word. This gives seven columns and the numbering of the columns will be:

P R O J E C T

5 6 4 3 2 1 7

For every seven letters in the message you will need one line of 'boxes' to write down the message, so other rules to remember are:

1 Count the number of letters in the original message.

2 Divide this number by the number of letters in the key word.

This will give you the number of horizontal lines required when drawing the 'boxes'. If there is a number left over from the division, this will mean that one more line is required.

As long as the key word remains a secret between yourself and the person you are sending the messages to, it is unlikely that anyone else will be able to break the code unless he or she is quite clever at the art. You may not want to take a chance on this, though, and in that case you want to be able to change the key word frequently.

You can play this two ways. You can agree on different key words for different days, or use some familiar and easy-to-remember key words and a double code.

Project

Using the days of the week

Suppose we use the days of the week for key words. MONDAY will be the key word for messages written on Monday, TUESDAY for Tuesday's messages, and so on. To keep it simple we will send just a short secret message—SEE YOU TONIGHT.

First write down the key word—MONDAY. Work out the letter order in figures

M O N D A Y
3 5 4 2 1 6

Now draw up the table and write in the message, as in figure 5. The coded message becomes:

OG YI STT EN EO UH

Draw up a second table, just like the first, and write this coded message in the 'boxes' (figure 6). From this, extract the final coded message to send:

SO IE OTH YN GE TU

This should have fooled most people. Even if they guessed that you were using MONDAY as the key word and used this to decode the final message, they would have ended up with their message again as in our figure 5. They would have got:

OGYISTTENEOUH

. . . and that certainly does not make sense!

(figure 5)

M	O	N	D	A	Y
3	5	4	2	1	6
S	E	E	Y	O	U
T	O	N	I	G	H
T	o	n	i	g	h

(figure 6)

M	O	N	D	A	Y
3	5	4	2	1	6
O	G	Y	I	S	T
T	E	N	E	O	U
H					

They would immediately think that you were using a different code word, and probably give up.

Project

Keep it a secret

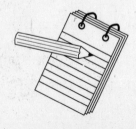

Remember, that other people will be reading this book and will know about this trick of double coding.

Work out some other variations that are known only to yourself and your friend. Then nobody else will be in on the secret.

PART THREE

MORE LETTER CODES

Another type of coding system that uses a key word is the cipher alphabet, which is used, letter by letter, to turn a plain message into a coded one. Only the person knowing the key word can work out the actual cipher alphabet used.

Project

The cipher alphabet

First start with a key word—say ALPHABET this time. Write this down, leaving out any letters that have already appeared in the line. With Alphabet, the letter 'A' appears twice, so the second 'A' is left out.

Now work out the order of the rest, just

(figure 7)

1	5	6	4	2	3	7
A	L	P	H	B	E	T

(figure 8)

1	5	6	4	2	3	7
A	L	P	H	B	E	T
C	D	F	G	I	J	K
M	N	O	Q	R	S	U
V	W	X	Y	Z		

as you did in Part Two, but put them on top of the letters this time.

Divide this up into seven columns with vertical lines and draw a horizontal line under the figures. Draw another horizontal line under the letters, and then three more horizontal lines to make 'boxes' (figure 7).

Fill in these boxes with all the other letters of the alphabet, in correct order, but leaving out all those that have already appeared in the key word. Thus 'A' and 'B' are both in the key word, but 'C' is not. Start with a 'C' in the first box, then 'D', and so on, to end up like figure 8.

This cipher alphabet is read downwards, in columns, just as before, but this time including the key word as well. The columns are read in the order of the numbers. So, first write down the ordinary alphabet and alongside this the cipher alphabet obtained from the table you have worked out.

This is the key to the whole code.

ordinary alphabet	becomes	cipher alphabet	
A		A	
B		C	
C		M	reading down column 1
D		V	
E		B	
F		I	reading down column 2
G		R	
H		Z	
I		E	
J		J	reading down column 3
K		S	
L		H	
M		G	reading down column 4
N		Q	
O		Y	
P		L	
Q		O	reading down column 5
R		N	
S		W	
T		P	
U		F	
V		O	reading down column 6
W		X	
X		T	
Y		K	reading down column 7
Z		U	

You can tear up the original table,
once you have worked out the cipher
alphabet.

Your friend will also need a copy of this
alphabet, or he or she can work it out in the
same way, once you have passed on, or
decided on, the key word.

To write a message in code, the letters in
the plain message are simply replaced
with those that they become in the cipher
alphabet.

The message: THIS IS CIPHER ALPHABET CODE
becomes: PZEW EW MELZBN AHLZACBP MYVB

This may look like simple letter shift,
described in Part One, but is really quite
different.

Every letter in the coded message has a
different shift, so it is not really a shift at all. It is
letter substitution, which is what a cipher
alphabet is, and that makes it a lot more difficult
to break the code.

Project

A code book

Once again you can use different key words for different days, so that you are always changing the cipher alphabets you are using.

Work out cipher alphabets for Monday, Tuesday, Wednesday, etc, as the key words. Write these alphabets down in your own secret notebook, which then becomes a code book. Use the code book for coding messages according to the day of the week they are sent.

Work out other cipher alphabets for different code words that you can change to if you think that someone has broken your code, or has happened to guess the key word and the fact that you are using a cipher alphabet and not letter substitution.

Everyone who uses a code or cipher knows that there is always the chance that it may be broken, so you should always be prepared to change the key word, or method, you are using. You have already learnt three quite different methods of making codes, and there are still more you can try.

PART FOUR

ALPHABET TABLES

An alphabet table, or Vigenère table as it is sometimes called, gives twenty-six different cipher alphabets (the same number as there are letters in the alphabet), each one associated with a key letter.

It is drawn up by writing the alphabet in the usual way horizontally, and vertically, around the edge of a square.

```
        A B C D E F etc
    A
    B
    C
    D
    etc
```

The square is then filled in line by line, starting the cipher alphabet in each line with the key letter, which is the letter in the vertical column down the side of the square.

	A	B	C	D	E	F	G	H	I	etc
A	A	B	C	D	E	F	G	H	I	etc
B	B	C	D	E	F	G	H	I	J	etc
C	C	D	E	F	G	H	I	J	K	etc
D	D	E	F	G	H	I	J	K	L	etc

A complete square looks like this:
Message letters

```
  A B C D E F G H I J K L M N O P Q R S T U V W X Y Z
A A B C D E F G H I J K L M N O P Q R S T U V W X Y Z
B B C D E F G H I J K L M N O P Q R S T U V W X Y Z A
C C D E F G H I J K L M N O P Q R S T U V W X Y Z A B
D D E F G H I J K L M N O P Q R S T U V W X Y Z A B C
E E F G H I J L K M N O P Q R S T U V W X Y Z A B C D
F F G H I J K L M N O P Q R S T U V W X Y Z A B C D E
G G H I J K L M N O P Q R S T U V W X Y Z A B C D E F
H H I J K L M N O P Q R S T U V W X Y Z A B C D E F G
I I J K L M N O P Q R S T U V W X Y Z A B C D E F G H
J J K L M N O P Q R S T U V W X Y Z A B C D E F G H I
K K L M N O P Q R S T U V W X Y Z A B C D E F G H I J
L L M N O P Q R S T U V W X Y Z A B C D E F G H I J K
M M N O P Q R S T U V W X Y Z A B C D E F G H I J K L
N N O P Q R S T U V W X Y Z A B C D E F G H I J K L M
O O P Q R S T U V W X Y Z A B C D E F G H I J K L M N
P P Q R S T U V W X Y Z A B C D E F G H I J K L M N O
Q Q R S T U V W X Y Z A B C D E F G H I J K L M N O P
R R S T U V W X Y Z A B C D E F G H I J K L M N O P Q
S S T U V W X Y Z A B C D E F G H I J K L M N O P Q R
T T U V W X Y Z A B C D E F G H I J K L M N O P Q R S
U U V W X Y Z A B C D E F G H I J K L M N O P Q R S T
V V W X Y Z A B C D E F G H I J K L M N O P Q R S T U
W W X Y Z A B C D E F G H I J K L M N O P Q R S T U V
X X Y Z A B C D E F G H I J K L M N O P Q R S T U V W
Y Y Z A B C D E F G H I J K L M N O P Q R S T U V W X
Z Z A B C D E F G H I J K L M N O P Q R S T U V W X Y
```

Project

Using the alphabet table

To use the alphabet table to write a message in code, just decide on a key letter. The line of letters in the table against this key letter is then the cipher alphabet to use.

Use the key letter F, and the cipher alphabet is then 'F' for A, 'G' for B, and so on.

If the message was:

GOING HOME

the code message, with the key letter F used, would be

LTNSL MTRJ

We would also add the key letter to the message, so that the person who received it would know which line to look at in the alphabet table to decode the message. Why not run all the letters together to make it look a little more confusing:

FLTNSLMTRJ

This code is not too difficult to break, but we can make it more difficult by using a different key letter for each word. Suppose we stick to F for the first word, and use the key letter V for the second word. We then get:

FLTNSL VCJHZ

Notice that we have added the key letter at the front of each word.

Now run all the letters together:

FLTNSLVCJHZ

That looks almost impossible to decode! But if the recipient has an alphabet table, he or

she will know that line F in the table is the key for the first word. When a letter appears on the end of the word he is decoding, which is obviously wrong and does not belong to the word, he knows this is the key letter for the next word, and so on.

Project

Your own key letters and phrases

Use this form of coding with different key letters and your own phrases to practise turning any message quickly into a secret code.

Project

Your own alphabet table

Work out your own alphabet table using a different arrangement of letters in each line. These letters, which form the cipher alphabets, can be in any order. The chances of any two people working out the same table in this way are millions to one.

Work out other ways you can use your alphabet table, double-coding or re-coding around another key word perhaps. It is no good telling you exactly how to do this. It will only be secret if you work it out for yourself.

PART FIVE

DOUBLE-CODING WITH ALPHABET TABLES

The basic alphabet table given in Part Four is almost a code book in itself and has one other advantage. If you lose it, you can easily work out another table.

To make it more secret, you need a simple way of using the various key letters that tell which line of cipher alphabet is being used without giving this away in the coded message.

The answer is double-coding, using a key word that does not appear in the coded message at all.

As long as only two people know the key word being used, they will be the only ones who know which key letter is being used to turn each letter of the plain message into the coded message.

First decide on a key word—say PROJECT. Write down the message and above this write the key word, letter above letter, repeating the key word as many times as necessary.

Key word (repeated):
P ROJE CTP RO JECT PROJECT

Message:
I WILL NOT BE HOME TONIGHT

Now each letter from the key word, above the message letter, is the key letter for turning that message letter into its cipher alphabet letter.

Starting with the first letter, which is 'I', the key letter above 'I' is P. From line P in the alphabet table, I is 'X', so the coded message starts with 'X'. The next letter is 'W', and the key letter above it is 'R'. So 'W' becomes 'N'.

The complete message coded in this way becomes:

X NWUP PGI SS QSOX IFBRKJM

Now people looking at this coded message will probably guess that it uses letter substitution, which it does. But every letter is substituted in a different way, so they will not get very far trying to break a code like this. Their next guess may be that you have used an alphabet table, and the first or last letter may be the key letter. They will not get anywhere like this either, even if they try every key letter in the table in turn. The key changes with each letter, so by double-coding you have produced a fairly safe message, and using the alphabet table has made it quite easy for someone who knows the code to work out.

It is just as easy to decode, once the person receiving the message knows what the key word is. He or she simply writes down the message and above it, letter by letter, the key word.

Key word:
P ROJE CTP RO JECT PROJECT

Coded message:
X NWUP PGI SS QSOX IFBRKJM

The decoder can then look up the equivalent letters in the alphabet table. For a start, he or she knows that the first letter 'X' in the coded message is from line P (key letter P) in the alphabet table. Looking this up in the table shows that 'X' stands for 'I'. The decoder then does the same for every other letter, in turn, until the whole message has been deciphered.

Once again, of course, the key word used can be changed from time to time, or even every day. The days of the week could be the key words for each day. Because it is difficult to spot that a message like this is double-coded, this fairly obvious choice of key words should still be quite safe. To make it even safer, you could agree to use the days of the week as key words and spell them out backwards. Another method is to use the name of the day ahead, or the day behind, for the key word for each day. Thus on Monday you would use TUESDAY as the key word, and on Tuesday you would use WEDNESDAY, and so on.

Project

Your own scheme

Work out your own scheme for key words. The whole object of a key word is that it should be known only to the people you want to understand your code.

Key words can be long or short. Just repeat them over and over, as necessary, to match the length of the message letter by letter. It is best if the key word contains all different letters, as this will mean that every letter in the message is changed or substituted in a different way, although this is not essential.

Project

Substitute numbers

You can use key words with an alphabet table you have worked out for yourself, as explained in Part Four. Try introducing numbers as well as letters in such a table to make the cipher alphabets even more confusing. This would enable you to replace up to eight letters in any one line in the complete table. You cannot use '1' (figure one) as this would be confused with 'I' (letter); or '0' (nothing or zero) which would be confused with 'O' (letter).

PART SIX

The Playfair cipher

This is a well-known double-code, but since it uses a code word and has so many possible variations, it is a very tough one to break. It has the advantage over alphabet tables that only a small 'key' table is required, based on twenty-five squares.

Project

Preparing a new key table

How to prepare this key table is shown in figure 9. First draw out twenty-five squares in a box shape. Decide on a key word and write

(figure 9)

C	I	P	H	E
R	A	B	D	F
G	K	L	M	N
O	Q	S	T	U
V	W	X	Y	Z

this down, letter by letter, in the top line of squares, continuing on to the next line if necessary. Letters in the key word that have already been written down are left out if they occur again in the word.

You can of course choose your own key word, but as an example we will use the word CIPHER. Write this down, as shown, in the squares, and fill in the rest of the squares with the remaining letters of the alphabet that have not already appeared in the key word, in their alphabetical order, but leave out J. You then have a complete square of twenty-five different letters. If the letter 'J' appears in your original message, call it 'I' instead.

The message is written down, say:

SMITH WENT TO THE SHOP

and then split up into groups of two letters each:

SM IT HW EN TT OT HE SH OP

Any group that has double letters has one of these letters replaced by X. This happens in the fifth group of our message, so rewrite the message:

SM IT HW EN XT OT HE SH OP

If the message had worked out to leave a single letter at the end instead of a pair, an X would have had to be added to make this last group a pair.

Each pair of letters in the message is then replaced by its cipher pair, following two basic rules:

The pair of letters together with the cipher pair either:

1 form the sides of a four-letter square, reading from left to right or top to bottom. If you like, you can think of this as the two pairs of letters together forming a four-

letter line, either horizontally reading from left to right, or vertically reading from top to bottom;

2 form opposite diagonals of a square or rectangle within the key drawing.

WORKING OUT A MESSAGE

Let us take the message, group by group, and work it out (figure 10). SM makes a diagonal in the four-letter 'square' LMTS. The corresponding cipher pair must therefore be the other diagonal, LT.

IT makes a diagonal in a twelve-letter rectangle IHTQ. HQ is the opposite diagonal and thus the cipher pair.

HW makes a diagonal in rectangle IHYW. IY is the opposite diagonal and thus the cipher pair.

(figure 10)

EN lies in a vertical line. To complete a four-letter line, we have EFNU. The other two letters in this line, FU, are thus the cipher pair.

XT is another diagonal, giving SY as the cipher pair.

OT lies on a horizontal line. To complete a four letter line we have Q and S between them. QS is thus the cipher pair.

HE lies on a horizontal line. Remember we have to read from left to right, so go back to the beginning of the line for the 'follow on' pair of letters, CI, which is the cipher pair.

SH is another diagonal, with the cipher pair PT.

Finally, OP forms the corners of a twelve-letter rectangle, so the cipher pair is CS. The completely coded message then reads like this:

LT HQ IY FU SY QS CI PT CS

Being in pairs does perhaps give the game away as to what type of cipher has been used, but that will not be a great deal of help to anyone trying to break the code because the table that gives the answer to cipher pairs is based on a secret key word.

To make it a little more confusing, run all the cipher pairs together:

LTHQIYFUSYQSCIPTCS

or split them up into groups of five:

Note the two letters that were added to the last group. They do not mean anything and are just added for effect and to confuse anyone who is looking for the key to the code.

Using the table properly to plan a Playfair cipher does need a little practice, but once you are used to it you will find it quicker and easier than alphabet tables.

To decode the message you must have the table again to refer to. The coded message is then split up into groups of two letters, if it is not already in this form. All that then remains to be done is to find the equivalent pairs of the cipher pairs, in the same way as for coding.

49

The most likely mistake in coding, and decoding, is reading the opposite pair of letters the wrong way round. This will not usually matter as the mistake is generally obvious when reading the decoded message.

Project

Different square-tables

Vary this code by using different key words to draw up different twenty-five square-tables of letters. Also jumble up the remaining letters of the alphabet that follow the key word. They do not have to run in alphabetical order, but it makes it a lot easier to work out a table if they do, then, if you want to change the key word, all you need tell your friend is the new key word so that he or she can work out a new table.

If you use a 'mixed' alphabet you will need to make a copy for your friend to work with. If this gets lost, then he or she will not be able to decode your messages, or code messages to send back to you in the Playfair cipher. Working to a simple alphabetical order, the table can be worked out again anywhere, from the key word.

PART SEVEN

Code breaking

There are two basic ways of breaking or deciphering a coded message when you do not know what the code is. The first is to try to find out what method of coding is being used, and from that find the code by trial and error. The second is to work simply on the coded message itself and try to solve it by the *principle of frequency.*

Guessing the code, the first method, is only likely to work when a very simple code is being used, like the simple letter codes described in Part One. In the case of a more complicated code, it may be possible to guess the type of code, but this may not be a great help if a key word is also involved. To solve the code means guessing the key word as well.

Guessing is not quite the hit-or-miss method it may seem. Once you know the various types of codes and how to use them, as described earlier, you are making a calculated guess at what the code might be.

If you are right, this is the simplest and quickest method of breaking a code. And even if you can only find the type of code being used, this is a help. You will know whether or not to stop there and apply the 'frequency' method to try to complete breaking the code.

Look for clues

Code-breaking is much harder than code-making, for there are no definite rules you can apply, apart from looking for clues and working the other way round. That is, having learnt how to make various codes, you will have learnt which ones depend on key letters and where these key letters are most likely to appear in the message.

It is really a special type of detective work, looking for clues and making intelligent guesses at what the code writer has probably done. Some people are very good at code-breaking, others get nowhere with it, just as some people are good at crossword puzzles and others are not. But to become a good code-breaker needs a great deal of patience and determination.

Project

Breaking a code

Start with this coded message:

VJKU OGUUCID KU VTKVVGP KP EQFG

What sort of code does this look like? Well, it seems to be individual words because the number of letters in each group is different. It may, therefore, be simple letter shift. Let us try and see, starting with a one-letter shift forward, that is, A written as B, B as C, and so on.

Write out the alphabet on a strip of paper, as in figure 11, so that you can spot shifts with a pencil to make the job easier.

A one-letter shift would make the first word:

UIJT

Obviously that is not right, so let us try a one-letter shift backwards. A becomes Z, B becomes A, etc. That makes the first word:

WKLV

That does not make sense either. But this is not taking very long to check, so let us now try a two-letter shift forward, with A becoming C, B becoming D, and so on. This makes the first word:

THIS

It looks as if we have broken the code. Now proceed with the two-letter shift.

THIS MESSAGE IS WRITTEN IN CODE

That's it! We have decoded the message.

Project

Work out these codes

Here are three more coded messages all using letter shift. Work them out for yourself. You should be able to break these quite easily, except for one. The first word works out all right, once you have found the correct shift, but the next word is then obviously wrong. Can you find out why? Perhaps this code is using a different 'shift' for each word? Write out the alphabet on a piece of paper and use a pencil to count shifts (figure 11).

(figure 11)

A B C D E F G H I J K L M N O P Q R S T U V W X Y Z

Message 1:   PIXXIV WLMJX GSHI YWIH

Message 2:   DBO AQW JXHVV UIJT POF

Message 3:   RHMFKDRGHESNMKX

Do not be fooled by this last one. It is still a letter shift code, even if all the letters are run together. This means that the words will all run together when decoded. If you want to cheat the solutions are at the end of the chapter.

THE PRINCIPLE OF FREQUENCY

Where straightforward guesswork does not work, the principle of frequency must be applied to code-breaking. This is based on the frequency with which the letters of the alphabet appear in typical messages, some letters obviously being used more than others in writing words.

All types of simple substitution codes, letters substituted for other letters, can be solved by the frequency method, even if they are based on key words, or key letters in the case of alphabet tables.

This does not mean that solving these codes will be easy. It can take a very long time, especially if the coded message is short. The shorter the message the more the frequency ratio of letters can be upset. In typical message writing, the letter Z is likely to appear only once in a thousand letters, and the letter E as many as 125 times. A message like this would completely upset the frequency ratio:

LAZY ZOO ANIMAL

The Z appears twice in 13 words, and E does not appear at all!

THE FREQUENCY TABLE

Messages written for coding are usually slightly different from the wording that would be used for ordinary writing or in books. The frequency table, therefore, is based on the typical appearance of letters in telegraphic and similar communications and is based on the number of times each letter is likely to appear in a thousand letters. This is far longer than any coded message is likely to be, so we can reduce this to 100 letters as a better guide for working on code-breaking, although this should eliminate entirely from the list those letters that appear less than 10 times per thousand on average. These are X, K, Q, J and Z. We shall have to include them with a rating of 1 though. The completed frequency table is shown on page 50.

DOUBLE LETTERS

In short messages, double letters will upset the frequency table figures, but they are easy enough to spot as double letters. They do not lend themselves to making into a frequency table of their own in short messages, but the common ones are likely to be EE, TT, SS and LL. It really depends on what type of message you write.

Project

Double letters

When you write messages, make a note of the double letters you use in each message. Keep a record, and when you have written a hundred different messages, add up the number of times each double letter has been used and make up your own frequency table for double letters.

BREAKING THE CODES BY FREQUENCY

In any simple substitution code or cipher, the fact that the letters in the original message have all been changed into other letters does not upset the principle of frequency. If E has become S, for example, it simply means that S will probably appear with the greatest frequency in the coded message. Work on this coded message as an example (Message 1 which we have already solved by the guessing method).

PIXXIV WLMJX GSHI YWIH

There are only eighteen letters in this message, so we cannot expect the frequency code to apply exactly, for it would need a thousand letters or more in the message for it to do so.

First, count the number of times each letter

FREQUENCY TABLE

	number of times appearing in 1000 letters	number of times appearing in 100 letters
E	125	12
T	90	9
R	83	8
I	76	8
N	75	7
O	74	7
A	72	7
S	58	6
D	40	4
L	36	4
C	33	4
H	33	3
F	30	3
U	30	3
P	27	3
M	25	2
Y	21	1
G	18	1
W	14	1
V	13	1
B	11	1
X	5	1
K	3	1
Q	3	1
J	2	1
Z	1	1

appears: P–1, I–4, X–3 (including a double letter), V–1, W–2, L–1, J–1, G–1, S–1, H–2, Y–1.

Now rearrange them in frequency order: I–4, X–3, H–2, W–2, G–1, J–1, L–1, P–1, S–1, Y–1.

Compare this with the frequency table. 'I' at the top of the list would be E, if the frequency table is working. So substitute E for I in the coded message:

PEXXEV WLMJX GSHE YWEH

'X' is next with three appearances, and if the frequency code table is working this could be 'T'. It also appears as a double letter, and 'TT' is a common double letter.

PETTEV WLMJT GSHE YWEH

The first word already looks promising. It could be BETTER or LETTER.

Try 'H' and 'W' as 'R' or 'I', again working from the frequency table. Write down your own answers. These do not make sense. The frequency table therefore is not working this time, until we come to try 'W' equals 'S'.

PETTEV SLMJT GSHE YSEH

Now is the time to try some guesswork. Suppose the first word is LETTER. The message could then start LETTER SENT, but it cannot be that for we already know that 'I' is 'E', so 'L' cannot be 'E' in the second word and the word has to have 5 letters. Try another word for S***T—say SHIFT, making the start LETTER SHIFT.

Can you guess your way through the rest of the message in this way?

There is also another way to work on guessing. The frequency table has given a possible starting word, or most of it anyway. See if this fits in with a standard method of coding, say letter shift. If it does, see if the rest of the message works out.

The frequency method used alone will never give a complete answer, except in freak cases. You will have to start guessing and changing, and trying different alternatives. It can be a long business. But the real experts can break any simple substitution code this way, even though it may take them days or weeks.

SOLUTIONS TO CODES ON PAGE 56

1 Letter shift code used. A shift of 4 letters backwards was used.

2 Can you guess this one? The first word was a shift of 1 letter back; the second word a shift of 2 letters back; the third word a shift of 3 letters back; the fourth and fifth words a shift of 1 letter back.

3 SINGLE SHIFT ONLY. A shift of one letter forward was used.

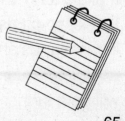

PART EIGHT

MORE 'TRICKS OF THE TRADE'

Where a coded message is obviously written in word groups, then a short cut to decoding is often guessing what a double letter word probably is—IN, OF, TO, and so on.

Project

More ways to help break down codes

You made a list of double letters and prepared your own frequency table for them in Part Seven. Make a further list of those two-letter words that appear in messages and draw up another frequency table for them. This will be a further help to you for code-breaking.

This works both ways as well. The more you learn about code-breaking, the more you will know what clues to look for. The 'give-away' double letters and common words eventually become easy to guess. You can use this knowledge when you are writing a coded message by making sure you avoid these 'give-away' combinations. The more you can avoid E's, T's and I's, for example, in the plain message, the more difficult it will be for anyone to solve the code using the frequency table.

We have also seen that word groups in themselves can be a give-away, which is why coded messages are often spelt out in groups of five letters or all the letters run together. This eliminates word clues. You can break up the original words into different lengths, like this:

Message:
SEND IT OFF TODAY

Rewritten for coding:
SE NDIT OFFT OD AY

Another easy method is to add odd letters that mean nothing and are easily spotted as meaning nothing when the message is decoded:

Message:
> *SEND IT OFF TODAY*

Rewritten for coding:
> SENDXITYOFFZTODAY

There is also the simple method of breaking up double letters by designating them with an X before the letter, thus XT instead of TT, XO instead of OO, and so on. This should make the double-letter frequency table quite useless, unless the person trying to break the code happens to guess what you have done.

Keep the message short

One of the main things to remember is that the shorter the message, the more difficult it will be to break, unless you are using a simple letter-shift code. That is fairly easy to discover by trial-and-error methods. Also, if in a short message you try to get the frequency of the letters used in the original message quite different from those of the frequency table, the code may become virtually unbreakable, except to an experienced cryptographer, even if it is quite a simple code type you are using.

Double-coding, using a key word, is virtually unbreakable by any amateur cryptographer, unless he or she happens to be able to guess the key word used.

Project

Using the shift code

Start with this plain message
and write it out in simple letter shift code:

*CAN YOU DECODE THIS
MESSAGE EASILY*

See how many ways you can do this using
the same code each time and get a friend to
decode the two or three you think
include the least number of
'give-aways'. Tell your friend it
is only a simple letter-shift
code. If he or she can
break each one quite
easily, your method of
disguising the clues is not
very good.

Get your friend to write
disguised messages in
simple codes for you
to break. The more
practice you can get,

both in making and breaking codes, the better. It will also show which of the simpler codes can most easily be made unbreakable, and working with simple codes is much easier than using the more complicated ones.

PART NINE

MECHANICAL CODES

Mechanical codes can be made virtually unbreakable without having the key mechanism on which they were made, since they do not follow frequency tables or letter substitution methods. They do, in fact, just appear as a random collection of letters.

Project

Making a cipher machine

To make a cipher machine, all you need is a paper streamer and a length of wood dowel, about 2–2.5 centimetres (3/4–1 inch) in diameter and 30 centimetres (12 inches) long. Wind the paper round the dowel in the form of a spiral, each turn close against the next, but not overlapping, as shown in figure 12. Write the message, letter by letter, in a line along the length of the spiral, one letter on each width of streamer.

72

(figure 12)

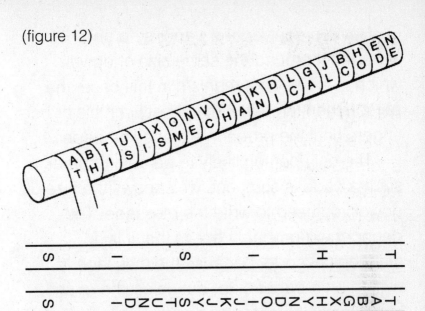

Unwrap the streamer and lay it out flat. The message will appear on the paper with large gaps between each letter. Fill in these spaces with other letters so that you end up with a strip of paper filled with letters from top to bottom.

The only way to decode this message is to wrap it around the same size of dowel as was first used in writing the message, in the same spiral fashion. This will produce a 'cylinder' of paper with lines of letters running from end to end. One, and only one, line of letters will be the original message (figure 13). All the other lines will not read properly.

Having received the paper strip and wrapped it around the same size of dowel, which is the key mechanism in this case, the person then turns the dowel between his or her fingers until the proper message line appears.

The only person likely to be able to break such a code is someone who knows the size of dowel you used to write the message. The decoder will probably guess that it is a mechanical code, because the message is written on a paper strip, but unless he or she has exactly the same size of dowel, the original message cannot be re-formed unless you have accidentally left some further clues.

(figure 13)

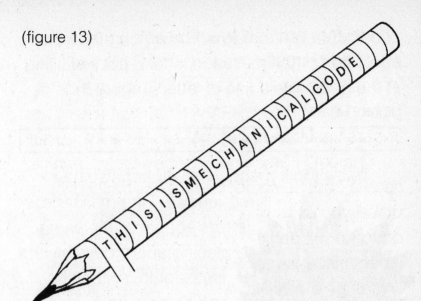

USE A PENCIL

For short messages you could use a pencil instead of a dowel, but this is an obvious choice of key mechanism and would be the first thing anyone trying to break a code like this would attempt.

You may also have left a clue by the way you have filled in the intermediate letters. The message has been written with the paper curved around a dowel, and the others have been written with the paper flat. This could show up as slightly different shapes in the letters or as different spacing, which produces gaps and indicates where the significant letters occur. This you can avoid by adding letters on each side of the message letters, not just filling in the gaps with a line of letters (figure 14).

(figure 14)

× × × — × × × × ⊗ × × × × — × × × × ⊥ × × × × ⊣ ⊔ ⑁ ⅏

This simple mechanical cipher also has a frequency. All the message letters appear at the same spacing apart, possibly the first, eighth, sixteenth, and so on, with a frequency spacing of eight in this case. To break the code, different frequency spacings would have to be tried in turn to see if they worked out and eventually gave a proper message. This may take a long time, but the code could be broken in this way. You can make it much more difficult to break if you add letters to the paper strip before the start of the message and at the end. This gives a false frequency spacing for a start, which can make the real frequency spacing almost impossible to find.

Project

Mechanically coded messages

Work out some mechanically coded messages using a dowel or a similar long cylindrical object as the key mechanism. The larger the diameter of the key mechanism, the higher the frequency spacing and the more difficult the code will be to break. On the other hand, you will need a very long strip of paper to complete the message.

Project

Key mechanisms

You do not have to use a round object for the key mechanism. In figure 15 you can see how to make your own key mechanism from balsa sheet, which you can cut to a special width. The edges must be rounded so that the paper streamer can be wrapped around without creasing at the edges, as this could be a give-away as to the width of the key piece. It is important that you make two identical strips, both rounded off in exactly the same way. If not, the paper will not wrap round in exactly the same way, and the letters will not lie in proper lines.

Writing the message on a flat strip key piece is easier than using a rounded key. You can also write in all the other lines of mixed letters while the paper strip is still in position on the key.

(figure 15)

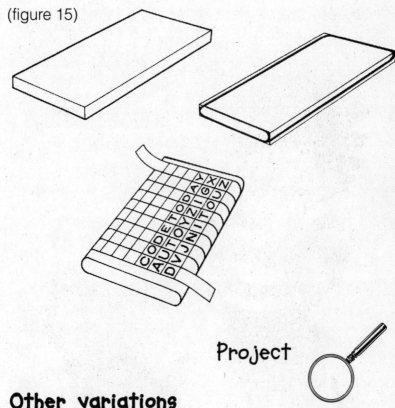

Project

Other variations

Can you work out other variations on this idea?

How could you use a mechanical key like this to construct cipher alphabets? Work this out for yourself and see how you can use a mechanical key for double-coding.

PART TEN

NUMBER CODES

Number codes are commonly used for sending straight messages. That is to say, the messages are not secret, they are meant to be understood by everyone who knows the number code.

The numbers are simply a compact way of sending information by telegraph, radio or teleprinter, each number representing a word or giving some particular information.

One of the most widely used number codes is that used by meteorological stations and meteorological offices all over the world. Weather reports are sent in number codes,

giving information on wind, sky and temperature in a fraction of the time it would take to give the same information in words.

Numbers cannot be used as direct substitution for letters in making up a code, for there are not enough of them. It would be difficult to use a two-figure number as a substitute for a letter, owing to the possibility of confusion if a two-figure number and a single-figure number were accidentally run together or misread as three separate numbers. There is no real advantage in substituting numbers for letters in making codes. There are enough possible variations with letter substitution to make as many secret codes as anyone is ever likely to want. And when numbers have to be sent in a letter code message, they are simply spelt out—one, two, etc.

NUMBERS FOR NON-SECRET CODES

Number codes are normally used only for non-secret codes that simply convey information in a compact manner. The same thing could be done with letters, but random number sequences are easier to speak and remember than random arrangements of letters.

Project

Letters and numbers

Try this for yourself. Most people can easily remember a sequence of up to seven numbers, having heard them or read them once. Can you read this number sequence and then write it down on a piece of paper without a mistake?

2 0 9 7 4 6 5

Now try the same thing with letters:

D N H K W C F

This is not as easy. See how many numbers you can memorise in a single reading and compare this with the number of random letters you can memorise. You may be quite surprised at the difference. The reason for this is that with numbers you have only ten different ones to deal with, but with letters there are twenty-six. It should be two-and-a-half times more difficult to memorise random letters than random numbers.

Project

Using number codes

Number codes are very useful when making notes as they can save several words. All you have to do is to work out a standard code or key as to what the numbers are to mean and then use them.

Devise a number code as a rating for how well the school football team played in each match during the term. You could use the following ratings:

Brilliant   5
Very good   4
Good   3
Fair   2
Poor   1
Hopeless   0

On your fixture card, when you record the score, add the number code rating for the match. There will be room for this where there might not be room for words.

At the end of the season you can look back through the fixture card and see immediately which were the good matches and which the less good ones. You could work out an average for the whole term by dividing the total of number ratings by the number of matches, and compare with the previous term's performance.

Project

Experimenting with number codes

Work out other ways in which you can use number codes to help you keep records and notes. It is easy to remember numbers, and so codes like this are very quickly learnt. You have

only to put them down at the front or back of your notebook as a reminder in case you do forget, as this can happen if you use several different number codes.

Unbreakable number codes

Numbers can be used to produce a completely unbreakable coded message, provided the key remains secret. The key is a book, in fact any book of which you and your friend each have a copy.

For simplicity, assume that you are going to use a single-number code, which means that the code message will consist of three-figure groups, like this:

129 215 616

In each group:

1 The first number relates to the number of a page in the book. You can start from page 1, when '1' means page 1, or agree to start from page 10, when '1' would mean page 10; or agree to start from page 100, when '1' would mean page 100.

2 The second number then means the number of lines down on that page. Thus 2 would mean line 2.

3 The third number gives the number of words in, along that line. Thus 9 would be the ninth word in line 2 on page 1 (or 10 or 100).

USING A BOOK CODE

What we have described, in fact, is the way the message is decoded. To code it, decide on a page number to start with and note that number. Then find the word you want to use and put down what line it appears on (the second number) and then how many words along that line it is (the third number).

You should, within the first nine lines on any page of most books, find all the words you would want to use in a message, and so a simple single-figure coding system should be suitable.

If not, it may be easier to change the wording of the message slightly rather than adopt a more elaborate figure coding.

There is nothing wrong with using a more elaborate figure coding. Although it may be giving the game away by making it clearer that you are using figures to refer to book pages, lines, and words along that line, this will not help anyone trying to break the code if he or she does not know what the book is.

If you use more than single-figure codes, you should separate each number with an

oblique stroke. The message groups might then work out something like this

124/12/8 26/17/3 and so on.

You can easily work out what the above means.

The first group means that the first word is on page 124, on the 12th line, and is the 8th word along in that line.